This book belongs to:

Mina

This book is dedicated
to magical creatures everywhere.

Published in 2019 by Flowered Press
Copyright 2019 by Hayley Rose

Text and design by Hayley Rose
Illustrations by Lynx Studios

ISBN: 978-0-999-8073-7-8
Library of Congress Cataloging-in-Publication Process

The Thankful Mermaid:
I Am Kind

By Hayley Rose

Illustrated by Lynx Studios

Date 2021

Today I am thankful for:
1. My mom.
2. My dog.
3. My toys.

My dreams and goals:
1. to listen more.
2. to make srue your kind.
3. to give the dog more love.

today

What I love about myself:
1. That I listened a lot
2. that im buitiful.
3. that I have a great mom.

My affirmations:
1. that I am alive.
2. that I don't live alon
3. that my dog helps Me.

"What wisdom can you find that is greater than kindness." ~ Jean Jacques Rousseau

Date 2021

Today I am thankful for:
1. the food that I eat.
2. The water that I dink.
3. that I have a great mom.

My dreams and goals:
1. to be patient.
2. to play with the dog more.
3. to be less sad.

What I love about myself:
1. that I care about my dog.
2. that I care about my friend
3. that I care about my family.

My affirmations:
1. I am happy to be alive.
2. I am happy that I have
3. I am happy that I god.

have friends.

"Its not what happens to you, but how you react to it that matters." ~ Epictetus

Date 2021

Today I am thankful for:

1. My home.
2. Moms money.
3. My room.

My dreams and goals:

1. to think befor' you say stuff.
2. to control yourself.
3. to be more happy.

What I love about myself:

1. that I am good at art.
2. that I am good at reading.
3. that I am good at writing.

My affirmations:

1. that I am happy to be alive
2. to eat good food.
3. to drink pink lemoniade.

"Let us be grateful to people who make us happy. They are the charming gardeners who make our souls blossom." ~ Marcel Proust

Date 2021

Today I am thankful for:
1. My friends.
2. My family.
3. My teacher.

My dreams and goals:
1. to be nice to mean people.
2. to help around the house.
3. to do more art.

What I love about myself:
1. that i'm good at cheer.
2. that I eat healthy.
3. that my mom loves me.

My affirmations:
1. that I am happy.
2. that I am alive.
3. that I have a nice mom.

"The essence of all beautiful art, all great art, is gratitude." ~ Friedrich Nietzsche

Date _____

Today I am thankful for:

1. _____
2. _____
3. _____

My dreams and goals:

1. _____
2. _____
3. _____

What I love about myself:

1. _____
2. _____
3. _____

My affirmations:

1. _____
2. _____
3. _____

"Be happy. Live thankful." ~ The Thankful Mermaid

Date _____

Today I am thankful for:

1. _____
2. _____
3. _____

My dreams and goals:

1. _____
2. _____
3. _____

What I love about myself:

1. _____
2. _____
3. _____

My affirmations:

1. _____
2. _____
3. _____

"As a man thinketh in his heart, so shall he be." – James Allen

Date _____

Today I am thankful for:

1. _____
2. _____
3. _____

My dreams and goals:

1. _____
2. _____
3. _____

What I love about myself:

1. _____
2. _____
3. _____

My affirmations:

1. _____
2. _____
3. _____

"The key to happiness is living with a grateful heart." ~ The Thankful Mermaid

Date _____

Today I am thankful for:

1. _____
2. _____
3. _____

My dreams and goals:

1. _____
2. _____
3. _____

What I love about myself:

1. _____
2. _____
3. _____

My affirmations:

1. _____
2. _____
3. _____

"A person is only by the thoughts that he chooses." ~ James Allen

Date _____

Today I am thankful for:

1. _____
2. _____
3. _____

My dreams and goals:

1. _____
2. _____
3. _____

What I love about myself:

1. _____
2. _____
3. _____

My affirmations:

1. _____
2. _____
3. _____

"Happiness is a habit—cultivate it." ~ Elbert Hubbard

Date _____

Today I am thankful for:

1. _____
2. _____
3. _____

My dreams and goals:

1. _____
2. _____
3. _____

What I love about myself:

1. _____
2. _____
3. _____

My affirmations:

1. _____
2. _____
3. _____

"Wonder is the desire for knowledge." ~ Thomas Aquinas

Date _____

Today I am thankful for:

1. _____
2. _____
3. _____

My dreams and goals:

1. _____
2. _____
3. _____

What I love about myself:

1. _____
2. _____
3. _____

My affirmations:

1. _____
2. _____
3. _____

"You are today where your thoughts have brought you." ~ James Allen

Date _____

Today I am thankful for:

1. _____
2. _____
3. _____

My dreams and goals:

1. _____
2. _____
3. _____

What I love about myself:

1. _____
2. _____
3. _____

My affirmations:

1. _____
2. _____
3. _____

"Gratitude is the fairest blossom which springs from the soul."
~ Henry Ward Beecher

Date _____

Today I am thankful for:

1. _____
2. _____
3. _____

My dreams and goals:

1. _____
2. _____
3. _____

What I love about myself:

1. _____
2. _____
3. _____

My affirmations:

1. _____
2. _____
3. _____

"He is greatest whose strenght carries up the most hearts by attraction of his own."
~ Henry Ward Beecher

Date _____

Today I am thankful for:

1. _____

2. _____

3. _____

My dreams and goals:

1. _____

2. _____

3. _____

What I love about myself:

1. _____

2. _____

3. _____

My affirmations:

1. _____

2. _____

3. _____

"Our life is what our thoughts make it." ~ James Allen

Date _____

Today I am thankful for:

1. _____
2. _____
3. _____

My dreams and goals:

1. _____
2. _____
3. _____

What I love about myself:

1. _____
2. _____
3. _____

My affirmations:

1. _____
2. _____
3. _____

"A man is literally what he thinks." ~ James Allen

Date _____

Today I am thankful for:

1. _____

2. _____

3. _____

My dreams and goals:

1. _____

2. _____

3. _____

What I love about myself:

1. _____

2. _____

3. _____

My affirmations:

1. _____

2. _____

3. _____

"Kindness in words creates confidence. Kindness in giving creates love." ~ Lao Tzu

Date _____

Today I am thankful for:

1. _____
2. _____
3. _____

My dreams and goals:

1. _____
2. _____
3. _____

What I love about myself:

1. _____
2. _____
3. _____

My affirmations:

1. _____
2. _____
3. _____

"Dream lofty dreams, and as you dream, so you shall become, your vision is the promise of what you shall one day be." ~ James Allen.

Date _____

Today I am thankful for:

1. _____
2. _____
3. _____

My dreams and goals:

1. _____
2. _____
3. _____

What I love about myself:

1. _____
2. _____
3. _____

My affirmations:

1. _____
2. _____
3. _____

"All that a man achives and all that he fails to achieve is the direct result of his own thoughts." ~ James Allen

Date _____

Today I am thankful for:

1. _____
2. _____
3. _____

My dreams and goals:

1. _____
2. _____
3. _____

What I love about myself:

1. _____
2. _____
3. _____

My affirmations:

1. _____
2. _____
3. _____

"No duty is more urgent than that of returning thanks." ~ James Allen

Date _____

Today I am thankful for:

1. _____
2. _____
3. _____

My dreams and goals:

1. _____
2. _____
3. _____

What I love about myself:

1. _____
2. _____
3. _____

My affirmations:

1. _____
2. _____
3. _____

"Dwell in a place of gratitude and you will always be home."
~ The Thankful Mermaid

Date _____

Today I am thankful for:

1. _____
2. _____
3. _____

My dreams and goals:

1. _____
2. _____
3. _____

What I love about myself:

1. _____
2. _____
3. _____

My affirmations:

1. _____
2. _____
3. _____

"What wisdom can you find that is greater than kindness." ~ Jean Jacques Rousseau

Date _____

Today I am thankful for:

1. _____
2. _____
3. _____

My dreams and goals:

1. _____
2. _____
3. _____

What I love about myself:

1. _____
2. _____
3. _____

My affirmations:

1. _____
2. _____
3. _____

"Its not what happens to you, but how you react to it that matters." ~ Epictetus

Date _____

Today I am thankful for:

1. _____
2. _____
3. _____

My dreams and goals:

1. _____
2. _____
3. _____

What I love about myself:

1. _____
2. _____
3. _____

My affirmations:

1. _____
2. _____
3. _____

"Let us be grateful to people who make us happy. They are the charming gardeners who make our souls blossom." ~ Marcel Proust

Date _____

Today I am thankful for:

1. _____

2. _____

3. _____

My dreams and goals:

1. _____

2. _____

3. _____

What I love about myself:

1. _____

2. _____

3. _____

My affirmations:

1. _____

2. _____

3. _____

"The essence of all beautiful art, all great art, is gratitude." ~ Friedrich Nietzsche

Date _____

Today I am thankful for:

1. _____
2. _____
3. _____

My dreams and goals:

1. _____
2. _____
3. _____

What I love about myself:

1. _____
2. _____
3. _____

My affirmations:

1. _____
2. _____
3. _____

"Be happy. Live thankful." ~ The Thankful Mermaid

Date _____

Today I am thankful for:

1. _____
2. _____
3. _____

My dreams and goals:

1. _____
2. _____
3. _____

What I love about myself:

1. _____
2. _____
3. _____

My affirmations:

1. _____
2. _____
3. _____

"As a man thinketh in his heart, so shall he be." – James Allen

Date _____

Today I am thankful for:

1. _____
2. _____
3. _____

My dreams and goals:

1. _____
2. _____
3. _____

What I love about myself:

1. _____
2. _____
3. _____

My affirmations:

1. _____
2. _____
3. _____

"The key to happiness is living with a grateful heart." ~ The Thankful Mermaid

Date _____

Today I am thankful for:

1. _____
2. _____
3. _____

My dreams and goals:

1. _____
2. _____
3. _____

What I love about myself:

1. _____
2. _____
3. _____

My affirmations:

1. _____
2. _____
3. _____

"A person is only by the thoughts that he chooses." ~ James Allen

Date _____

Today I am thankful for:

1. _____
2. _____
3. _____

My dreams and goals:

1. _____
2. _____
3. _____

What I love about myself:

1. _____
2. _____
3. _____

My affirmations:

1. _____
2. _____
3. _____

"Happiness is a habit–cultivate it." ~ Elbert Hubbard

Date _____

Today I am thankful for:

1. _____
2. _____
3. _____

My dreams and goals:

1. _____
2. _____
3. _____

What I love about myself:

1. _____
2. _____
3. _____

My affirmations:

1. _____
2. _____
3. _____

"Wonder is the desire for knowledge." ~ Thomas Aquinas

Date _____

Today I am thankful for:

1. _____
2. _____
3. _____

My dreams and goals:

1. _____
2. _____
3. _____

What I love about myself:

1. _____
2. _____
3. _____

My affirmations:

1. _____
2. _____
3. _____

"You are today where your thoughts have brought you." ~ James Allen

Made in the USA
Middletown, DE
20 December 2020